GREAT MINDS® WIT & WISDOM

# Grade 4 Module 3:
## The Redcoats Are Coming!

*Student Edition*

## COPYRIGHT STATEMENT

# Table of Contents

Handout 1A: Readers' Theater

Handout 1B: Fluency Homework

Handout 2A: Perspectives Chart

Handout 3A: Perspectives Chart

Handout 3B: Frayer Model for *Liberty*

Handout 4A: "Massacre in King Street"

Handout 4B: Perspectives Chart

Handout 4C: Focusing Question Task 1: Evidence Organizer

Handout 6A: Explanatory Essay

Handout 6B: Identifying Fragments and Run-Ons

Handout 7A: Explanatory Writing Checklist

Handout 7B: Sorting Fragments, Run-Ons, and Complete Sentences

Handout 7C: Identifying Fragments, Run-Ons, and Complete Sentences

Handout 10A: Discussion Questions for *Colonial Voices*, Part 1

Handout 10B: Opinion Paragraphs

Handout 11A: Discussion Questions for *Colonial Voices*, Part 2

Handout 12A: Opinion Organizer

Handout 12B: Fluency Homework

Handout 13A: "Detested Tea"

Handout 13B: Hutchinson's Exemplar Opinion Letter

Handout 14A: Quotations Treasure Hunt

Handout 14B: Transitional Words and Phrases

Handout 15A: Opinion Writing Checklist

Handout 15B: Vocabulary Words

Handout 16A: Fluency Homework

Handout 17A: Punctuating Compound Sentences

Handout 19A: Essay Organizer

Handout 20A: Explanatory Writing Checklist

Handout 21A: Fluency Practice Homework

Handout 22A: *Woods Runner* Questions

Handout 22B: "Communication" in *Woods Runner*

Handout 23A: Author's Craft Scavenger Hunt

Handout 24A: Samuel

Handout 25A: Facts in Fiction

Handout 25B: Vocabulary Clarification

Handout 26A: Fluency Practice Homework

Handout 26B: Relative Adverbs and Clauses

Handout 31A: Opinion Writing Checklist

Handout 33A: End-of-Module Task Evidence Organizer

Handout 33B: Opinion Writing Checklist

Volume of Reading Reflection Questions

*Wit & Wisdom* Parent Tip Sheet

Name: _____

Date: _____

# Handout 1A: Readers' Theater

**Directions:** Read aloud with your class the part of the text labeled "All." Find the part that matches your assigned group (G1 or G2) and read it aloud with your group. Use appropriate expression as you read.

**All:** There were once two enemies who were both named George.

**G1:** George Washington was the man who freed the American colonies from the British.

**G2:** And George III was the British king who lost them.

**All:** Was King George a "Royal Brute?"

**G1:** American patriots said so.

**G2:** But others hailed him as "the Father of the People."

**All:** Was George Washington a traitor?

**G2:** The king's supporters thought so.

**G1:** But many celebrated Washington as "the father of his country."

**All:** Who was right?

**All:** There are two sides to every story.

George vs. George: The American Revolution as Seen from Both Sides, *Rosalyn Schanzer*

Name: _____

Date: _____

# Handout 1B: Fluency Homework

**Directions:**

1. Day 1: Read the text carefully and annotate to help you read fluently.
2. Each day:
   a. Practice reading the text aloud three to five times.
   b. Evaluate your progress by placing a checkmark in the appropriate, unshaded box.
   c. Ask someone (adult or peer) to listen and evaluate you as well.
3. Last day: answer the self-reflection questions at the end.

---

**Introduction**

Who could imagine that the fabric binding America to Great Britain was about to unravel or that the two Georges were about to become bitter enemies? Who could guess that George III would be the last king of America, and that George Washington would one day become its first president?

Neither George Washington nor King George III was fully responsible for everything that happened next. Many other thinkers, soldiers, and politicians helped to shape the future. Even so, as leaders of the two sides, these two Georges were to become the strongest symbols of their countries during the next 20 years. The different ideas they stood for would soon turn the whole world upside-down.

Schanzer, Rosalyn. *George vs. George: The American Revolution as Seen from Both Sides.* National Geographic Society. 2004.

---

Name: _____

Date: _____

| Student Performance Checklist: | Day 1 | | Day 2 | | Day 3 | | Day 4 | |
|---|---|---|---|---|---|---|---|---|
| | You | Listener* | You | Listener | You | Listener* | You | Listener* |
| Accurately read the passage three to five times. | | | | | | | | |
| Read with appropriate phrasing and pausing. | | | | | | | | |
| Read with appropriate expression. | | | | | | | | |
| Read articulately at a good pace, and an audible volume. | | | | | | | | |

*Adult or peer

**Self-reflection:** What choices did you make when deciding how to read this passage, and why? What would you like to improve on or try differently next time? (*Thoughtfully answer these questions on the back of this paper.*)

Name: _____

Date: _____

# Handout 2A: Perspectives Chart

**Directions:** Review pages 12–17 of *George vs. George: The American Revolution as Seen from Both Sides* to find evidence related to the different perspectives of the British and the colonists. Fill in the blanks with the missing words from each quote. Think about how each perspective may lead to conflict between the two sides. Circle the words that indicate or relate to perspective (how someone sees something, or thinks or feels about something).

| British Perspectives | Colonists' Perspectives |
|---|---|
| Thought of _____ as "the Father of the People" (Schanzer 7) | Thought _____ was "a Royal Brute" (Schanzer 7) |
| Thought _____ was "a traitor" (Schanzer 7) | Thought of _____ as "the father of his country" (Schanzer 7) |
| "...the English were _____ that the rest of the British Empire was _____ and _____." (Schanzer 13) | |
| "...throughout England, people...would soon _____ especially hard about the _____ over in America." (Schanzer 13) | "...the _____ over in America." (Schanzer 13) |
| Great Britain made a law that said the colonists couldn't settle the new territories. "London thought it was _____ and _____ to reserve these lands for the _____..." (Schanzer 15) | "Many colonists _____ to settle the new territory they had helped to win... George Washington agreed with plenty of other colonial settlers, who thought the law unfairly limited their _____ ..." They "poured into the west anyway." (Schanzer 15) |

Name: _____

Date: _____

| | |
|---|---|
| "King George tried hard…to see that _____ decisions agreed with his point of view… Even so, he had some very strong _____." (Schanzer 16) | |
| "For years England had _____ the other way…" (Schanzer 17) | "…colonists _____ British laws they didn't _____." (Schanzer 17) |

George vs. George: The American Revolution as Seen from Both Sides, *Rosalyn Schanzer*

Name: _____

Date: _____

# Handout 3A: Perspectives Chart

**Directions:** Review pages 18–22 of *George vs. George: The American Revolution as Seen from Both Sides* to find evidence related to the different perspectives of the British and the colonists. Fill in the blanks with the missing words and citations related to the quotations. Think about how each perspective may lead to conflict between the two sides. Circle the words that indicate or relate to perspective (how someone sees something, or thinks or feels about something).

## Part 1

| British Perspectives | Colonists' Perspectives |
|---|---|
| Parliament "decided that Americans should help out by paying their _____..."<br><br>"Great Britain had spent plenty of money fighting in America for the good of the colonies" and they thought "It was Great Britain's _____ to collect payment!" (Schanzer 18) | "The colonists were already paying separate taxes to cover their own war debts and to run the colonies... A lot of them thought paying twice wasn't one bit _____." (Schanzer _____) |
| "To raise the money, Parliament passed a _____ and a _____ saying that colonists had to pay taxes to Great Britain for all sort of imported goods..." (_____ 18) | "...they believed it was against the British Constitution ...The colonists were British citizens, and the law guaranteed them the 'rights of Englishmen'" which said "no _____ without _____." (_____ _____) |
| | "Though many colonists would stay _____ (loyal) to the crown and obey its laws no matter what, others argued that Parliament might make them pay even more taxes without their _____." (_____ _____) |

Name: _____

Date: _____

## Part 2

| British | Colonists |
|---|---|
| "Four months later, hoping to restore _____, Parliament finally gave up and got rid of the hated _____." (Schanzer 20)<br><br>"This troubled King George, who still thought the taxes were fair, but he signed the _____ anyway." (_____ 20) | "Many colonial merchants refused to _____ British goods." (Schanzer 19)<br><br>Groups of colonists, such as the Sons of Liberty, protested in different ways by writing pamphlets, preaching against the taxes, wrecking the home of the governor, burning the stamps, and flying flags at half-mast "to mourn the death of _____." (Schanzer _____)<br><br>"Nobody in America would even distribute the _____." (_____ 20) |
| "British merchants were _____ to get their lost customers back..." (Schanzer 20) | "...all of America _____." (Schanzer 20) |
| "To show they weren't afraid to tax the colonists, Parliament started _____ even more taxes." (_____ 20) | "Patriot leaders...made polite _____ to the king, but politeness didn't help one bit." (Schanzer _____) |

Name: _____

Date: _____

| | |
|---|---|
| "King George believed that God gave noblemen the _____ to rule and that the colonists had a duty to obey." (Schanzer 21)<br><br>"King George was sure that certain 'gentlemen who pretended to be patriots' in Massachusetts were no more than _____, so he sent a fleet of warships to Boston to make them _____." (Schanzer _____) | "Colonists _____ in untaxed goods from other countries, which was illegal." (Schanzer 21)<br><br>"...they made a lot of their own _____ (goods) instead of buying British ones." (Schanzer 21)<br><br>"...the _____ supported the cause by weaving their own cloth, making their own ball gowns, and brewing their own _____." (_____ 21) |
| Seven hundred British soldiers showed up in Boston and started doing things that bothered the colonists. (Schanzer 22) | The colonists were bothered by the British soldiers and wanted them to leave. (Schanzer 22) |
| "The _____ troops began firing into the crowd, and five colonists were _____." (_____ 22) | "In March 1770, an angry mob of American rowdies started _____ eight of King George's soldiers and pelting them with icy snowballs. Then someone threw a lump of wood at a _____ and knocked him flat." (Schanzer _____) |
| "...it stirred up plenty of _____ on both sides." (_____ _____) | "Furious _____ were quick to label this disaster 'the Boston _____,' and it stirred up plenty of anger on both sides." (_____ _____) |

*George vs. George: The American Revolution as Seen from Both Sides, Rosalyn Schanzer*

Name:

Date:

# Handout 3B: Frayer Model for *Liberty*

**Directions:** Use what you have learned from the text, *George vs. George: The American Revolution as Seen from Both Sides*, and about American symbols, to complete the Frayer Model for the word *liberty*.

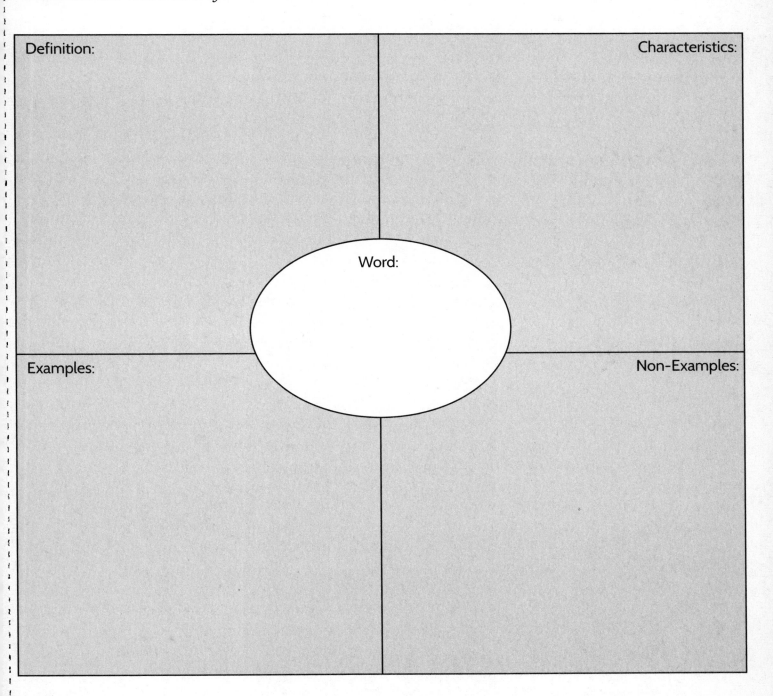

Name: _____

Date: _____

# Handout 4A: "Massacre in King Street"

**Directions:** Follow along as your teacher reads the article aloud.

British soldiers had been taunted by Boston's residents since their arrival in the city in October 1768. The troops had been sent to help Massachusetts acting governor Thomas Hutchinson keep law and order in the rebellious city. But Boston citizens resented their presence.

The Sons of Liberty met often to talk about what they should do. Samuel Adams felt that if the townspeople became angry enough, they might be ready to separate from Britain. Small fights between soldiers and citizens began to occur with some frequency. On March 5, 1770, events reached a boiling point.

The city was covered with a layer of new snow. Outside the Customs House on King Street, a barber's apprentice, Edward Garrick, shouted at a British soldier, Hugh White. Angered by the insult, White struck Garrick with the butt of his rifle. Garrick yelled for help, and a crowd gathered. Bells in a nearby church started ringing, sounding an alarm in the city, and more people rushed to the scene. White called for help, and eight additional soldiers came to his aid.

By some estimates, a mob of almost 400 people crowded around the British soldiers outside the Customs House. In addition to shouting insults at the soldiers, the crowd began throwing things—a stone, some ice, a snowball. The soldiers had been ordered not to fire, but the colonists grew more menacing. One gun went off, followed by others. The crowd dispersed only when Hutchinson promised that the eight soldiers and their captain would be arrested and tried for their actions. By morning, five colonists were dead, and six others were wounded.

For the soldiers' own safety, their trials were postponed a few months so that the Boston citizens could calm down. Hutchinson was forced to remove the troops from the city, which was a victory for the Sons of Liberty. However, the troops did not return to Britain. Instead, they moved to Castle William, an island in Boston Harbor.

Name:

Date:

John Adams, Samuel Adams' cousin, believed that Britain's actions in the Colonies were unjust. But John was a lawyer, and he believed that laws, not propaganda, would solve the problems. John and Josiah Quincy agreed to be the defending lawyers at the soldiers' trials. They convinced the jury that the soldiers had fired in self-defense. Only two of the men were found guilty of manslaughter. They were branded on the hand, a common form of punishment in those days, and discharged from the army.

The Boston Massacre, known at the time as the Bloody Massacre in King Street, was just one of a number of events that contributed toward a complete break with Great Britain. The loss of life that occurred made it stand out. And the Sons of Liberty organized a propaganda effort to put the blame for the deaths on the shoulders of the British soldiers.

Clemens, Mark. "Massacre in King Street." Cobblestone, Sept. 2014. Cricket Media, *Carus Publishing Company.*

Name: _____

Date: _____

# Handout 4B: Perspectives Chart

**Directions:** Review the article "Massacre in King Street" by Mark Clemens to find evidence related to the different perspectives of the British and the colonists. Fill in the blanks with the missing words and citations related to the quotations. Think about how each perspective may lead to conflict between the two sides. Circle the words that indicate or relate to perspective (how someone sees something, or thinks or feels about something).

| British Perspectives | Colonists' Perspectives |
|---|---|
| "British soldiers had been _____ by Boston's residents since their arrival in the city in October 1768." (Clemens "Massacre in King Street")<br><br>"The troops had been sent to help Massachusetts acting governor Thomas Hutchinson keep _____ in the rebellious city." (Clemens "_____") | "...Boston citizens _____ their presence." (Clemens "Massacre in King Street")<br><br>"The Sons of Liberty met often to talk about what they should do. Samuel Adams felt that if the townspeople became _____ enough, they might be ready to _____ separate from Britain." (_____ "Massacre in King Street") |
| "Angered by the _____, White struck Garrick with the butt of his rifle." (Clemens "Massacre in King Street") | "...a barber's apprentice, Edward Garrick, _____ at a British soldier, Hugh White." (Clemens "Massacre in King Street")<br><br>"Garrick yelled for _____, and a crowd gathered." (_____ "Massacre in King Street") |

Name: _____

Date: _____

| | |
|---|---|
| "White called for help, and eight additional soldiers came to his _____." (Clemens "Massacre in King Street")<br><br>"The soldiers had been ordered not to fire, but the colonists grew more _____. One gun went off, followed by others." (Clemens "Massacre in King Street") | "Bells in a nearby church started ringing, sounding an _____ ... and more people rushed to the scene." (Clemens "Massacre in King Street")<br><br>"...a mob of almost 400 people _____ around the British soldiers... In addition to shouting insults at the soldiers, the crowd began throwing things—a stone, some ice, a snowball." (Clemens "_____") |
| | "Hutchinson promised that the eight soldiers and their captain would be _____ and tried for their actions." (Clemens "Massacre in King Street")<br><br>"By morning, _____ colonists were dead, and six others were wounded." (Clemens "Massacre in King Street") |
| "However, the troops did not return to _____. Instead, they moved to Castle William, an island in Boston Harbor." (Clemens "Massacre in King Street") | "For the soldiers' own safety, their trials were postponed a few months so that the Boston citizens could _____." (Clemens "Massacre in King Street")<br><br>"Hutchinson was forced to remove the troops from the city, which was a _____ for the Sons of Liberty." (Clemens "Massacre in King Street") |

Name: _____

Date: _____

| | |
|---|---|
| "Only two of the men were found _____ of manslaughter. They were branded on the hand, a common form of punishment in those days, and discharged from the army." (Clemens "Massacre in King Street") | "John Adams, Samuel Adams' cousin, believed that Britain's actions in the Colonies were _____. But John was a lawyer, and he believed that laws, not _____, would solve the problems." (Clemens "Massacre in King Street") <br><br> "John and Josiah Quincy agreed to be the defending lawyers at the soldiers' trials. They convinced the jury that the soldiers had fired in _____." (Clemens "Massacre in King Street") |
| | "...the Sons of Liberty organized a propaganda effort to put the _____ for the deaths on the shoulders of the British soldiers." (_____ "_____") |

"Massacre in King Street," Mark Clemens

Name: _____

Date: _____

# Handout 4C: Focusing Question Task 1 Evidence Organizer

**Directions:** Research the two texts and the artwork to find evidence of the British and colonists' perspectives related to the conflicts which led up to the American Revolution. Reference also your Perspectives Charts. Record the perspectives on the left and the results on the right. Cite sources and page numbers for each entry.

**Question/Purpose: What were the perspectives of the two main sides of the American Revolution?**

| Context | Evidence | Elaboration/Explanation | Source, page number |
|---|---|---|---|
| Which side? | What was the perspective? (what was felt, thought, or believed; how something was seen) | What happened as a result of these perspectives? (the actions, decisions, conflicts, etc.) | Where did you find this information? |
| British | | | |
| Colonists | | | |

Name:

Date:

| British | |
|---------|---|
|         |   |
|         |   |
| Colonists | |

Name: _____

Date: _____

| | |
|---|---|
| | |
| | |
| | |
| **British** | **Colonists** |

Name: _____

Date: _____

| | |
|---|---|
| | |
| | |
| **British** | **Colonists** |

Name: _____

Date: _____

| | |
|---|---|
| | |
| | |
| | |
| **British** | **Colonists** |

Name: _____

Date: _____

# Handout 6A: Explanatory Essay

**Directions:** Write an explanatory essay to respond to the following prompt: What were the perspectives of the two main sides of the American Revolution?

Title: _____

| Introduction |
| --- |
| Thesis |
| Supporting Point 1 |
| Supporting Point 2 |

| Supporting Paragraph 1 |
| --- |

Name:

Date:

| Supporting Paragraph 2 |
| --- |
| Conclusion |

Name: _____

Date: _____

# Handout 6B: Identifying Fragments and Run-Ons

**Directions:** Read the following groups of words. Write "FR" next to each fragment, "RO" next to each run-on, and "CS" next to each complete sentence. Answer the question at the bottom.

1. A mob of almost 400 people crowded around the British soldiers outside the Customs House. _____

2. In addition to shouting insults at the soldiers. _____

3. The soldiers had been ordered not to fire, but the colonists grew more menacing, so one gun went off, followed by others, and the crowd dispersed only when Hutchinson promised that the eight soldiers and their captain would be arrested and tried for their actions. _____

4. A stone, some ice, a snowball. _____

5. By morning, five colonists were dead, and six others were wounded. _____

Why is it important to avoid fragments and run-ons when writing?

_____

_____

_____

"Massacre in King Street" by Mark Clemens

Name: _____

Date: _____

# Handout 7A: Explanatory Writing Checklist

**Directions:** Use this checklist to revise your writing. Mark + for "yes" and Δ for "not yet." Ask someone (adult or peer) to evaluate your writing as well.

| Reading Comprehension | Self +/ Δ | Peer +/ Δ | Teacher +/ Δ |
|---|---|---|---|
| I read texts and find evidence to explain the British perspectives and resulting events leading up to the American Revolution | | | |
| I read texts and find evidence to explain the colonists' perspectives and resulting events leading up to the American Revolution | | | |
| **Structure** | | | |
| I use the format of an introduction, two supporting paragraphs, and a conclusion | | | |
| I include a context, a focus statement, and two supporting points in my introduction that link to the two supporting paragraphs | | | |
| I develop supporting paragraphs that include a context, topic sentence, evidence and elaboration, and a conclusion | | | |
| My conclusion paragraph relates to my introduction and wraps up the essay | | | |
| I use context and transitions to link paragraphs and ideas | | | |
| **Development** | | | |
| I develop my topic with evidence from at least two texts | | | |
| My evidence is related to the topic | | | |
| I elaborate upon evidence by explaining or analyzing it | | | |

Name: _____

Date: _____

| Style | | | |
|---|---|---|---|
| I use a variety of sentence patterns (simple, compound, complex) | | | |
| I use at least three of the following vocabulary words: *conflict, perspective, convinced, massacre, propaganda, liberty, revolution, independence, taunted* | | | |
| My writing style is appropriate for the audience | | | |
| **Conventions** | | | |
| I use complete sentences in my writing and avoid the use of fragments and run-ons | | | |
| I use correct spelling, capitalization, and punctuation | | | |
| **Research** | | | |
| I gather relevant information from at least two sources as evidence for my supporting paragraphs | | | |
| **Total # of +'s** | | | |

Name: _____

Date: _____

# Handout 7B: Sorting Fragments, Run-Ons, and Complete Sentences

**Directions:** Cut out each group of words. Place each into a pile as a fragment, run-on, or complete sentence.

----------------------------------------------

1. For the soldiers' own safety, their trials were postponed a few months, so that the Boston citizens could calm down, and Hutchinson was forced to remove the troops from the city, which was a victory for the Sons of Liberty.

----------------------------------------------

2. However, the troops did not return to Britain.

----------------------------------------------

3. An island in Boston Harbor.

----------------------------------------------

4. John Adams, Samuel Adams' cousin, believed that Britain's actions in the Colonies were unjust, and John was a lawyer, so he believed that laws, not propaganda, would solve the problems, and John and Josiah Quincy agreed to be the defending lawyers at the soldiers' trials.

----------------------------------------------

5. They convinced the jury that the soldiers had fired in self-defense.

----------------------------------------------

6. Only two of the men.

----------------------------------------------

7. They were branded on the hand, a common form of punishment in those days, and discharged from the army.

----------------------------------------------

*"Massacre in King Street" by Mark Clemens*

Name: _____

Date: _____

# Handout 7C: Identifying Fragments, Run-Ons, and Complete Sentences

**Directions:** Read the following groups of words. Write "FR" next to each fragment, "RO" next to each run-on, and "CS" next to each complete sentence. Answer the question at the bottom.

1. The Boston Massacre ... was just one of a number of events that contributed toward a complete break with Great Britain. _____

2. Massacre in King Street. _____

3. Known at the time as the Bloody Massacre. _____

4. The loss of life that occurred made it stand out. _____

5. The Sons of Liberty organized a propaganda effort to put the blame for the deaths on the shoulders of the British soldiers, and make it look like the colonists had no part in the blame, so the colonists would want to rise up and fight against the British, so that they could be free. _____

What makes a sentence complete and effective?

_____

_____

_____

*"Massacre in King Street" by Mark Clemens*

Name: _____

Date: _____

# Handout 10A: Discussion Questions for *Colonial Voices,* Part 1

**Directions:** Read through the discussion questions and jot down notes on the text as you reread the first half of *Colonial Voices: Hear Them Speak.*

1. What is Ethan's job on this day?

_____

_____

_____

_____

2. What must Governor Hutchinson decide?

_____

_____

_____

_____

Name: _____

Date: _____

3. What historical facts are used in the monologues?

_____

_____

_____

_____

4. What are some of the different opinions colonists had about the tea tax?

_____

_____

_____

_____

Name: _____

Date: _____

# Handout 10B: Opinion Paragraphs

**Directions:** In each paragraph, highlight the opinion statement green. Find two reasons that support the opinion statement and highlight one yellow and one blue.

## Opinion Paragraph #1

Now that I have arrived in Boston, I understand what the captain meant when he said Boston is brewing with trouble. The family ordered to house me feeds me and has provided a firm bed, but it is obvious they do not want me here. I do not understand their opposition to us soldiers being stationed in Boston. Clearly the citizens need our protection from the craziness! The city is overrun with ruffians and thugs who are raising havoc at all hours of the night in protest of our presence. They are damaging or stealing the king's property and terrorizing the good citizens who support the Crown! I must always keep a watchful eye out for these trouble-makers to protect myself. It is a good thing the king sent us here to Boston before the whole city is destroyed!

## Opinion Paragraph #2

Now that Private Jones has arrived, our home is no longer ours. King George is trying to take over Boston one house at a time by forcing us to house his soldiers. I barely have enough food to feed my own children, and now I must feed a gluttonous soldier who eats everything in sight! Last night, he even brought to our home two other soldiers who were rude and disrespectful. They kicked my children and me out of our own house while they ate all the food I had prepared for dinner! I understand now why the Sons of Liberty have been sounding the alarm about this imposition of soldiers into our city. If we do not stand up to King George soon, Boston will no longer be in our control. Who does King George think he is to tax us unjustly and force us to care for his soldiers? This has to stop soon!

Name: _____

Date: _____

# Handout 11A: Discussion Questions for *Colonial Voices*, Part 2

**Directions:** Read through the discussion questions and jot down notes on the text as you reread the second half of *Colonial Voices: Hear Them Speak*.

1. Is the Midwife a Loyalist or a Patriot? How do you know?

_____

_____

_____

2. What do we learn about Loyalists from the Barber/Wigmaker?

_____

_____

_____

3. Is the slave a Loyalist, a Patriot, or In-Between? How do you know?

_____

_____

_____

Name: _____

Date: _____

4. What is an apprentice?

_____

_____

_____

5. What was Governor Hutchinson's decision?

_____

_____

_____

6. What is the secret Ethan delivered?

_____

_____

_____

7. How do the Patriots feel about the act of the "Tea Party"?

_____

_____

_____

Name: _____

Date: _____

# Handout 12A: Opinion Organizer

**Directions:** Write the name of your colonist at the top of the evidence organizer. Use your notes and texts to decide the political perspective of your colonist. Think about an opinion your colonist would have about the Boston Tea Party. Refer to your notes and your texts once again to identify two reasons that explain this opinion.

| |
|---|
| Monologue/Colonist: <br> The Shoemaker |
| Is your colonist a Patriot, Loyalist, or In-Between? <br> Patriot |
| Opinion Statement: <br> I think the british are unfair and we must stand up against them and fight for our freedom. |

| Reason #1 | Reason #2 |
|---|---|
| We are aready paying taxes to help pay off the war and the settling in america | we hav no-one to stand up for us in british pariment it is against the british constitution no taxation without representation |

Name: _____

Date: _____

# Handout 12B: Fluency Homework

**Directions:**

1. Day 1: Read the text carefully and annotate to help you read fluently.
2. Each day:
   a. Practice reading the text aloud three to five times.
   b. Evaluate your progress by placing a checkmark in the appropriate, unshaded box.
   c. Ask someone (adult or peer) to listen and evaluate you as well.
3. Last day: answer the self-reflection question at the end.

---

**The Milliner**

When we think of the milliner, we often think of hats. But hats were not the only item that decked her shop. Fabrics, shoes, jewelry, lace, gloves, and dishes were imported from England, France, and Italy. She also sold tobacco, handkerchiefs, stockings and neckwear for men. The milliner displayed dolls dressed in the latest styles for her customers to admire and order a similar gown. Some milliners employed mantua makers. These seamstresses designed and fit each dress to the customer. If the lady could not come to the shop, the mantua maker would go to the customer's home. Most milliners were women.

Winters, Kay. *Colonial Voices: Hear Them Speak.* Puffin Books, 2008.

---

| Student Performance Checklist: | Day 1 | | Day 2 | | Day 3 | | Day 4 | |
|---|---|---|---|---|---|---|---|---|
| | You | Listener* | You | Listener | You | Listener* | You | Listener* |
| Accurately read the passage three to five times. | | | | | | | | |
| Read with appropriate phrasing and pausing. | | | | | | | | |

Name: _____

Date: _____

| | | | | | | | | |
|---|---|---|---|---|---|---|---|---|
| Read with appropriate expression. | | | | | | | | |
| Read articulately at a good pace and an audible volume. | | | | | | | | |

*Adult or peer

**Self-reflection:** What choices did you make when deciding how to read this passage, and why? What would you like to improve on or try differently next time? (*Thoughtfully answer these questions on the back of this paper.*)

Name: _____

Date: _____

# Handout 13A: "Detested Tea"

**Directions:** Read the article "Detested Tea," including the "Thomas Hutchinson" text and other text features, and answer the questions on the New-Read Assessment handout.

**"Detested Tea," by Andrew Matthews**

> By the mid-1700s, tea was so popular in Great Britain and its colonies that it was considered the national drink. The decision to boycott tea shows the extent of American frustration with British policies.

The three ships tied up to Griffin's Wharf in Boston Harbor contained 342 chests that held 92,000 pounds of tea. Massachusetts governor Thomas Hutchinson was determined to get the cargo unloaded. Boston residents were equally determined to prevent that from happening. It turned into a historic standoff with dramatic results.

At issue was whether Great Britain had a right to collect a tax on certain items coming into the Colonies. In this case, the taxable item was tea—specifically, tea owned by the British East India Company.

The British East India Company had been around since the turn of the seventeenth century. But by the 1770s, it was heavily in debt, and the company held large amounts of surplus tea— about seventeen million pounds—in its warehouses.

Parliament decided to help the struggling company. The Tea Act of 1773 gave the British East India Company the right to ship tea directly to the Colonies instead of going to Great Britain first. It eliminated any duties to be paid by the company. It gave exclusive control for the sale of tea in the colonies to specific agents who were chosen by the king.

The law eliminated competition in the colonies and enforced the Townshend Acts from 1767, which included a tax on tea. Payment of the tax was expected to be made when the tea was unloaded or within twenty days of a ship's arrival. Parliament believed that when the colonists accepted this tax, they also would have to accept Parliament's right to impose taxes on them.

Name: _____

Date: _____

Except ... the colonists refused to pay the tax. Colonists convinced British East India Company agents and merchants to resign their positions. In New York, Philadelphia, Annapolis, and Charleston (South Carolina), the colonists refused the shipments of tea. They either sent them back to London, or they left the unloaded tea to rot on the docks.

But in Boston, Hutchinson and his sons, who had been appointed company agents, were not intimidated. When the first of three ships carrying tea arrived in late November, the citizens of Boston would not accept the cargo. They tried to send the ships back to Great Britain. But the ships were unable to leave without a pass from the governor, which Hutchinson refused to give until the tea was unloaded. So the ships sat in Boston Harbor.

As the twenty-day deadline approached, Boston's Sons of Liberty mobilized. On the evening of December 16, 1773, a crowd of men dressed as Mohawk Indians (to keep their identities a secret) approached the wharf. They instructed the men guarding the ships to step aside and asked for the keys to the holds. Working quickly and efficiently for three hours, they threw all the tea overboard. Only the tea and the chests it was in were destroyed. No other damage was done, except for a padlock owned by one of the ship captains. And that was replaced the next day.

The harbor was described as being so thick with tea that citizens later went out in small boats to slap the tea with oars to make sure it sank.

The Boston Tea Party was the first major act of defiance by colonists. The reaction from London was swift and severe. Parliament passed the Coercive Acts, which aimed to punish Boston. The port of Boston was closed until the value of the tea and the tax due on it was paid in full. For a city that relied on shipping and trade, it was a harsh blow. The Massachusetts colonial assembly was disbanded, ending the colony's ability to have a role in its government. And 4,000 British regulars were sent to Boston to police the colony. Boston citizens were expected to provide room and board for the soldiers.

---

**FAST FACT:** American merchants owned the ships holding the tea in Boston.

---

Name: _____

Date: _____

By December 21, Sons of Liberty member Paul Revere set out from Boston for New York City with word of the Boston Tea Party. News of Great Britain's reaction followed shortly. The Boston Tea Party helped unify the Colonies behind a common goal. Not only did the other colonies rally and send supplies to Boston's citizens, but they came together in their desire to resist British oppression. When Virginia's House of Burgesses voted to support Boston in 1774, Virginia's royal governor ordered that the colonial assembly be disbanded. In response, Virginia's leaders called for a meeting of the delegates from all the Colonies to discuss an organized plan of action. The First Continental Congress met in Philadelphia later that fall.

> **Did You Know?** Only one participant in the Boston Tea Party was arrested. Francis Akeley, a Sons of Liberty member, was jailed for his actions that night. He died on June 19, 1775, at the Battle of Breed's Hill.

## "Thomas Hutchinson," by Marcia Amidon Lusted

> "I doubt whether it is possible to project a system of government in which a colony 3,000 miles distant from the parent state shall enjoy all the liberty of the parent state." (Hutchinson)

Serving as lieutenant governor and then governor of Massachusetts from 1758 to 1774, Thomas Hutchinson became the focal point of colonial anger. While he had deep colonial roots, Hutchinson remained loyal to Great Britain. He thought the patriots were "hotheads" who used minor incidents to inflame public opinion against Britain. After his home was looted by an angry mob in 1765, Hutchinson secretly wrote to friends in Great Britain, urging the use of force to restrain the unruly Colonies. Some of his correspondence was released to the public, which further enraged Boston residents. Hutchinson's enforcement of the Tea Act in 1773, which led to the Boston Tea Party and the passage of the Coercive Acts, resulted in his exile to England.

*Matthews, Andrew. "Detested Tea." Cobblestone, Sept. 2014. Cricket Media, Carus Publishing Company.*

Name: _____

Date: _____

# Handout 13B: Hutchinson's Exemplar Opinion Letter

**Directions:** Use this exemplar opinion letter to analyze components of effective opinion writing.

December 17, 1773

Dear English Friends,

The Americans have gone mad! They have quarreled for years about the small taxes we have asked them to pay only to support their mother country. But the dumping of all that tea in the Boston harbor is an act of defiance that has gone too far! King George must use great force to stop this defiance and bring order back to the colonies. If something is not done soon, the Sons of Liberty will grow in power and those loyal to the king will be in great danger.

I believe the Sons of Liberty will stop at nothing to turn my fellow colonists against the king. Look, for example, at how they blamed the British soldiers for the death of a few traitors. Just as a matter of fact, it was the mob of rabble rousers who started the fight by throwing ice and blocks of wood at the soldiers. "Boston Massacre," indeed! The Sons of Liberty are masters at making the British Crown look bad. As a result, many of our own fellow governors are too scared to stand up for what is right. I will not abandon my mother country. My decision to make the colonists pay the taxes on the tea was justified. The Sons of Liberty must be stopped.

There is no doubt that it easy to stay loyal to the king. My own house was ransacked and I fear I will be tarred and feathered by these heathens just for completing my sworn duties to the king. In addition, they boycott English goods making it difficult for our law abiding citizens to make a living. To make matters worse, they also smuggle illegal goods from other countries and make their own tea. Although the king has sent soldiers to keep the piece, soldiers are not peace keepers, and our condition does not improve.

Name:

Date:

As I close this letter, please use whatever influence you have to convince the king that the time has come to use great force to regain control of the American colonies. Undoubtedly, the Sons of Liberty are growing in strength and numbers. England is the greatest power in the world and to have our young colonies rebel against us impacts our very core. If the king continues to wait, it will be too late.

Yours truly,
Thomas

Name: _____

Date: _____

# Handout 14A: Quotations Treasure Hunt

**Directions:** After all students in your class have counted off by five, use your student number and the chart to find your assigned texts. In your assigned text, look for memorable, remarkable, and meaningful quotations that support a possible theme.

|  | Text | Character |
|---|---|---|
| **Student #1** | *Colonial Voices* | Errand Boy<br><br>Mistress of School<br><br>Basket Trader<br><br>The Patriots |
| **Student #2** | *Colonial Voices* | Printer<br><br>Shoemaker<br><br>Tavern Keeper<br><br>Slave |
| **Student #3** | *Colonial Voices* | Baker<br><br>Milliner<br><br>Midwife<br><br>Clockmaker |
| **Student #4** | *Colonial Voices* | Barber/Wigmaker<br><br>Silversmith's Apprentice<br><br>Sons of Liberty |
| **Student #5** | *George vs. George* | Pages 18–25 |

Name: _____

Date: _____

When you find a strong quotation:

1. Write the quotation and monologue title (or page number) on a sticky note.

2. Place the sticky note on one of the colored charts to show if the quotation was said by a Patriot, Loyalist, or In-Between.

3. When everyone is finished finding quotations, discuss the theme for each group based on the quotations.

4. Using the marker, write one sentence on each chart that captures the theme for that group of people.

Name: _____

Date: _____

# Handout 14B: Transitional Words and Phrases

**Directions:** Use these transitional words and phrases to help organize and connect ideas in your opinion essay.

## Introducing Your Opinion:

| | | |
|---|---|---|
| In my opinion, | There is no doubt that | I question whether |
| I believe | From my point of view | I (dis) agree with |
| It is my belief that | It seems to me that | I maintain that |

## Introducing Your Reasons:

| | | |
|---|---|---|
| First, | Equally important | Besides, |
| In the first place, | Likewise | Next, |
| Furthermore, | In addition, | Moreover, |
| Secondly | Similarly, | Also, |
| Thirdly, | | |
| Finally, | | |
| Lastly, | | |

## Introducing Examples/Reasons:

| | | |
|---|---|---|
| For example, | For instance, | In support of this, |
| In fact, | As evidence, | |

Name: _____

Date: _____

## Counterargument:
## (What "they" say)

| | | |
|---|---|---|
| Opponents may | Say | However, |
| I realize some may | Believe | Yet, |
| I understand others | Feel | But, I doubt |
| Even though some | Maintain | Yet, I question |
| Although some may | Want | On the other hand |
| Some people | Favor | Nevertheless |
| Opponents may | Support | Even so, |
| Your idea to _____ deserves some merit | Argue | In spite of this, |
| | State | Conversely, |
| | | On the contrary, |

## Rebuttal:
## (What I say)

## Concluding your opinion:

| | | |
|---|---|---|
| For the reasons above, | In short, | In brief, |
| As you can see, | Without a doubt, | Undoubtedly, |
| As I have noted, | Obviously, | |
| In other words, | Unquestionably, | |
| On the whole, | | |

Name: _____

Date: _____

# Handout 15A: Opinion Writing Checklist

**Directions:** Use this checklist to revise your writing. Mark + for "yes" and Δ for "not yet." Ask someone (adult or peer) to evaluate your writing as well.

| Reading Comprehension | Self +/Δ | Peer +/Δ | Teacher +/Δ |
|---|---|---|---|
| Refer to details and examples from both literary and informational texts when explaining key points about the American Revolution. | | | |
| Explain historical events related to the American Revolution including what happened and why, based on specific information in a text. | | | |
| **Structure** | | | |
| I respond to all parts of the prompt | | | |
| I focus on my opinion throughout the piece | | | |
| I introduce the topic or text clearly in my introduction paragraph | | | |
| I state a clear opinion in my introduction paragraph | | | |
| I organize my ideas into body paragraphs | | | |
| My conclusion paragraph relates to my opinion | | | |
| I use transitions to link paragraphs as well as to link opinions to reasons | | | |
| **Development** | | | |
| I support my opinions with reasons | | | |
| I support my reasons with evidence from text(s) | | | |
| I elaborate upon evidence | | | |
| **Style** | | | |
| I use a variety of sentence patterns (simple, compound, complex) | | | |
| I use vocabulary words that are specific and appropriate to the content | | | |

Name: _____

Date: _____

| | | | |
|---|---|---|---|
| My writing style is appropriate for the audience | | | |
| **Conventions** | | | |
| I use complete sentences by correcting fragments and run-ons | | | |
| I use formal English in my letter | | | |
| I use correct spelling, capitalization, and punctuation | | | |
| **Writing Process** | | | |
| I revise and edit my writing using the checklist to make it the best I can | | | |
| **Total # of +'s** | | | |

Name: _____

Date: _____

# Handout 15B: Vocabulary Words

**Directions:** Stop and Jot: Review the list of vocabulary words. Jot ideas for using these words spoken by your character about the Boston Tea Party.

Role Play answering the following question: "What do you think your two characters would say in response to finding out about the Tea Party to each other?" Try to use as many vocabulary words listed below in your discussion.

**Vocabulary:**

perspective

devoted

liberty

freedom

massacre

revolution

standoff

mobilized

restrained

**Idioms:**

- "change is in the air"
- "the time has come"
- "make our mark"
- "tell the tale"
- "keep time"
- "deed is done"

Colonial Voices: Hear Them Speak, *Kay Winters*

Name: _____

Date: _____

# Handout 16A: Fluency Homework

**Directions:**

1. Day 1: Read the text carefully and annotate to help you read fluently.
2. Each day:
   a. Practice reading the text aloud three to five times.
   b. Evaluate your progress by placing a checkmark in the appropriate, unshaded box.
   c. Ask someone (adult or peer) to listen and evaluate you as well.
3. Last day: answer the self-reflection questions at the end.

---

So once a week at dusk, using their secret code, Maddy Rose hung out her stockings and petticoats in the same order as the real ships along the wharf. A petticoat was code for a lightweight friendly vessel from the colonies. A scarlet stocking hanging toe up meant a merchant vessel from the islands or foreign port. When the toe hung down, it meant the vessel was suspicious and needed watching. But when the ship was riding low in the water, it meant only one thing—heavy firearms for the British. That's when Maddy Rose would weight that stocking down with a cobblestone.

Hakes Noble, Trina. *The Scarlet Stockings Spy.* Sleeping Bear Press, 2004.

---

| Student Performance Checklist: | Day 1 | | Day 2 | | Day 3 | | Day 4 | |
|---|---|---|---|---|---|---|---|---|
| | You | Listener* | You | Listener | You | Listener* | You | Listener* |
| Accurately read the passage three to five times. | | | | | | | | |
| Read with appropriate phrasing and pausing. | | | | | | | | |

Name: _____

Date: _____

| | | | | | | | | |
|---|---|---|---|---|---|---|---|---|
| Read with appropriate expression. | | | | | | | | |
| Read articulately at a good pace, and an audible volume. | | | | | | | | |

*Adult or peer

**Self-reflection:** What choices did you make when deciding how to read this passage, and why? What would you like to improve on or try differently next time? *(Thoughtfully answer these questions on the back of this paper.)*

Name: _____

Date: _____

# Handout 17A: Punctuating Compound Sentences

**Directions:** Combine two simple sentences into a compound sentence using a comma and the coordinating conjunction in brackets. Then, answer the question at the bottom.

1. Something made her look across the Delaware toward New Jersey. Her heart nearly stopped! (29) [and]

_____

_____

_____

2. That night Jonathan didn't come. Maddy Rose kept watch for him long into that black night. (30) [yet]

_____

_____

_____

3. She held up her chin. Her bottom lip quivered. (38) [but]

_____

_____

_____

Name: _____

Date: _____

4. How proud and strong it flew, just like her father's chin. It was Maddy Rose's scarlet stockings flag. (47) [for]

_____

_____

_____

5. Why are compound sentences important?

_____

_____

_____

*Sentences adapted from excerpts from The Scarlet Stockings Spy, Trinka Hakes Noble

Name: _____

Date: _____

# Handout 19A: Essay Organizer

**Directions:** Use your notes and work with a partner to fill in this essay organizer.

| Introduction (Who is Maddy? What did Maddy think about the Revolution?): | |
|---|---|
| Maddy's perspective: | Research/prior knowledge I can include: |
| Maddy's actions: | Research notes I can include: |

Name:

Date:

Concluding sentence:

Name: _____

Date: _____

# Handout 20A: Explanatory Writing Checklist

**Directions:** Use this checklist to revise your writing. Mark + for "yes" and Δ for "not yet." Ask someone (adult or peer) to evaluate your writing as well.

| Reading Comprehension | Self +/Δ | Peer +/Δ | Teacher +/Δ |
|---|---|---|---|
| I read texts and find evidence to explain how Maddy's actions show her perspective about the American Revolution | | | |
| I explain historical events related to the American Revolution including what happened and why, based on specific information in a text | | | |
| **Structure** | | | |
| I use the format of an introduction, two supporting paragraphs, and a conclusion | | | |
| I include a context, a focus statement, and two supporting points in my introduction which link to the two supporting paragraphs | | | |
| I develop supporting paragraphs which include a context, topic sentence, evidence and elaboration, and a conclusion | | | |
| My conclusion paragraph relates to my introduction and wraps up the essay | | | |
| I use context and transitions to link paragraphs and ideas | | | |
| **Development** | | | |
| I develop my topic with evidence from at least two texts | | | |
| My evidence is related to the topic | | | |
| I elaborate upon evidence by explaining or analyzing it | | | |

Name: _____

Date: _____

| Style | | | |
|---|---|---|---|
| I use a variety of sentence patterns (simple, compound, complex) | | | |
| My writing style is appropriate for the audience | | | |
| **Conventions** | | | |
| I use complete sentences in my writing and avoid the use of fragments and run-ons | | | |
| I use a comma before my conjunction in a compound sentence. I underline the sentence and draw a box around the comma and conjunction | | | |
| I use correct spelling, capitalization, and punctuation | | | |
| **Writing Process** | | | |
| I use the writing checklist to revise and edit my essay to make it my best writing | | | |
| Total # of +'s | | | |

Name: _____

Date: _____

# Handout 21A: Fluency Practice Homework

**Directions:**

1. Day 1: Read the text carefully and annotate to help you read fluently.
2. Each day:
   a. Practice reading the text aloud three to five times.
   b. Evaluate your progress by placing a checkmark in the appropriate, unshaded box.
   c. Ask someone (adult or peer) to listen and evaluate you as well.
3. Last day: Fill out the reflection box at the end.

---

The forest was unimaginably vast, impenetrable, mysterious and dark. His father had told him that a man could walk west for a month, walk as fast as he could, and never see the sun, so high and dense was the canopy of leaves.

Even close to their homestead—twelve acres clawed out of the timber with a small log cabin and a lean-to for a barn—the forest was so thick that in the summer Samuel could not see more than ten or fifteen yards into it. Some oak and elm and maple trees were four and five feet in diameter and so tall and thickly foliaged their height could only be guessed.

A wild world.

Paulsen, Gary. *Woods Runner.* Random House Children's Books, 2010.

---

Name: _____

Date: _____

| Student Performance Checklist: | Day 1 | | Day 2 | | Day 3 | | Day 4 | |
|---|---|---|---|---|---|---|---|---|
| | You | Listener* | You | Listener | You | Listener* | You | Listener* |
| Accurately read the passage three to five times. | | | | | | | | |
| Read with appropriate phrasing and pausing. | | | | | | | | |
| Read with appropriate expression. | | | | | | | | |
| Read articulately at a good pace, and an audible volume. | | | | | | | | |

*Adult or peer

**Self-reflection:** What choices did you make when deciding how to read this passage, and why? What would you like to improve on or try differently next time? (*Thoughtfully answer these questions on the back of this paper.*)

Name: _____

Date: _____

# Handout 22A: *Woods Runner* Questions

**Directions:** Read chapters 1–3 in *Woods Runner*. Write complete sentences to answer each question. Use evidence from the story to support your ideas.

1. Use the information on pages 4–5 to describe the forest. Why was it dangerous? Cite specific evidence from the text.

The Forest was vast (Huge) The Forest was
mysterious and dark because very little
light came through the thick canary of leaves

2. What information is written on the paper that Isaac shares with Samuel's father and the other families in the settlement? How do the men react to the news?

_____

_____

_____

_____

3. On page 19, the text states, "He had seen no fresh sign until he came halfway up the fifth ridge . . ." Use the information in the rest of the paragraph to describe what sign means in the sentence. How does this help Samuel hunt?

_____

Name: _____

Date: _____

_____

_____

_____

4. What caused Samuel to worry about an attack on his settlement? Use the information on page 21 to help you. Cite evidence from the text.

_____

_____

_____

_____

Quick Write:

_____

_____

_____

Woods Runner, *Gary Paulsen*

Name: _____

Date: _____

# Handout 22B: "Communication" in *Woods Runner*

**Directions:**

1.  Reread the informational text called "Communication" on page 12 in *Woods Runner*.
2.  Record notes on the left side of the chart to explain what the text says.
3.  Then read pages 14–16 in *Woods Runner*.
4.  Find evidence in the story of the facts you learned about communication in colonial America from reading the informational text and record it on the right side of the chart.
5.  Complete the Quick-Write at the bottom.

| Do this side first! | Do this side second! |
|---|---|
| **"Communication," page 12** | **Pages 14–15** |
| How did people in colonial America get news? | What text evidence in the story relates to the facts about getting news? |

Name: _____

Date: _____

| What were two problems with this method of communication? | What text evidence in the story demonstrates the problems with this type of communication? |
|---|---|
| | |

Quick Write: How does this news affect Samuel and what he is thinking?

_____

_____

_____

_____

Name: _____

Date: _____

# Handout 23A: Author's Craft Scavenger Hunt

**Directions:** Scan chapters 1–3 of *Woods Runner* and find the best example for each type of author's craft that builds your understanding of the American Revolution. Write the example in the box. Then, explain how each helps you understand this story. Also record the page number on which you found each example.

| Author's Craft | Example in *Woods Runner* | What does this help you understand about the story related to the American Revolution? | Page |
|---|---|---|---|
| Figurative language such as a simile or metaphor | Moving Through the woods like a knife Through "water". | I can picture Samuel moving | 3 |
| Setting description using sensory details | | | |
| Context clues to define a key word | | | |
| Historic fact or information woven into story | | | |

Name:

Date:

| A character speaks using dialect (way of speaking that is unique to a region) | | | |
|---|---|---|---|
| Flashback (a memory) | | | |
| Foreshadowing (a hint of something to come in the story) | | | |

Name: _____

Date: _____

# Handout 24A: Samuel

## Part 1: Samuel's Thoughts and Actions

**Directions:** Read chapters 4–6 in *Woods Runner*. Record examples of what Samuel is thinking and doing as he looks for his parents. What do his thoughts and actions reveal about Samuel?

| Samuel's Thoughts | This shows that Samuel is _____ because | Page |
|---|---|---|
| | | 29 |
| | | 31 |
| | | 36 |
| | | 41 |

| Samuel's Actions | This shows that Samuel is _____ because | Page |
|---|---|---|
| | | 30 |

Name: _____

Date: _____

| | | 36 |
|---|---|---|
| | | 45 |

## Part 2: Samuel's Knowledge

**Directions:** Gather evidence of the knowledge Samuel has that he can use to help him find his parents. Then, answer the Question/Purpose prompt.

| Question/Purpose: What is the most important knowledge Samuel has that can help him find his parents? | | | |
|---|---|---|---|
| **Context** <br><br> What knowledge does Samuel have? | **Evidence** <br><br> Quotation and Paraphrasing | **Elaboration/Explanation** <br><br> Why is it important? | **Source** <br><br> *Woods Runner* page number |
| | | | Page 36 |
| | | | Page 34 |

Name: _____

Date: _____

| | | | Page 38 |
| | | | |
| | | | Page 42 |
| | | | |

Write an opinion statement to respond to the prompt.

_____

_____

_____

_____

Name: _____

Date: _____

# Handout 25A: Facts in Fiction

**Directions:** Scan chapters 7–9 of *Woods Runner* and find the best example that demonstrates the factual information Paulsen mentioned in each short text. Record the page number where you found the example. Then write a few sentences to explain how this information affected your understanding of the story.

| Informational Text | Example in *Woods Runner* That Reflects This Fact | Page |
|---|---|---|
| The World, page 46<br><br>"Native Americans fought on both sides," | | |
| Warfare, page 52<br><br>"It took a special kind of courage to stand ready [against the British army]" | | |
| Wounds, page 56<br><br>"Untreated battle wounds often led to gangrene, which causes the body to literally rot away," | | |

Name: _____

Date: _____

| American Spirit, page 65<br><br>"The Americans . . . had much higher morale [enthusiasm and loyalty] than the British." | | |
|---|---|---|
| How does Paulsen's use of factual information affect your understanding of the story? | | |

Woods Runner, *Gary Paulsen*

Name: _____

Date: _____

# Handout 25B: Vocabulary Clarification

**Directions:** As you are reading the text, look for words that are unfamiliar to you. List them in the left column. Then, using Outside–Inside Strategy, write your prediction of the word's meaning in the second column. Look up the word in the dictionary to confirm the meaning and write a quick shortened definition. Then, explain how understanding the meaning helps you understand the text.

| Unknown Words | Prediction–Based on Outside and Inside Clues | Quick Definition– Based on Dictionary | How does understanding this word help me understand the text deeper? |
|---|---|---|---|
|  |  |  |  |
|  |  |  |  |
|  |  |  |  |

Name:

Date:

Name: _____

Date: _____

# Handout 26A: Fluency Practice Homework

**Directions:**

1. Day 1: Read the text carefully and annotate to help you read fluently.
2. Each day:
   a. Practice reading the text aloud three to five times.
   b. Evaluate your progress by placing a checkmark in the appropriate, unshaded box.
   c. Ask someone (adult or peer) to listen and evaluate you as well.
3. Last day: fill out the reflection box at the end.

---

He lay under overhanging hazel brush and studied the farm—here, very close to the middle of the wild, was an almost perfect little farm.

It had been three days since Samuel left the men behind. He'd eaten more and more meat, become stronger and stronger, and, at last, couldn't stand the slowness of walking beside the ox. The men were in no particular hurry; or, as Coop said, "Still gonna be a war, catch it now or catch it later." And they had gear to move, so had to go slowly.

But Samuel had become more frantic with every step. At last, when they'd stopped to rest, he had told Coop he was going to take off on his own.

Paulsen, Gary. *Woods Runner.* Random House Children's Books, 2010.

---

Name: _____

Date: _____

| Student Performance Checklist: | Day 1 | | Day 2 | | Day 3 | | Day 4 | |
|---|---|---|---|---|---|---|---|---|
| | You | Listener* | You | Listener | You | Listener* | You | Listener* |
| Accurately read the passage three to five times. | | | | | | | | |
| Read with appropriate phrasing and pausing. | | | | | | | | |
| Read with appropriate expression. | | | | | | | | |
| Read articulately at a good pace, and an audible volume. | | | | | | | | |

*Adult or peer

**Self-reflection:** What choices did you make when deciding how to read this passage, and why? What would you like to improve on or try differently next time? *(Thoughtfully answer these questions on the back of this paper.)*

Name: _____

Date: _____

# Handout 26B: Relative Adverbs and Clauses

**Directions:** Circle the relative adverb in each of the following sentences. Underline the clause which follows the relative adverb and gives more information about the sentence. Then, answer the question at the bottom of the page.

1. "... the water drains off and there is a handy clearing ... where the lake was." (17)

2. "Samuel was just thirteen, but he lived on a frontier where ... someone his age was thirteen going on thirty." (34)

3. The author describes frontier life as a time when childhood seemed to end once children were old enough to do some chores. (34)

4. After waking Samuel didn't remember the reason why he had shot at an Indian.

Write at least one reason why relative adverbs are important:

_____

_____

_____

Woods Runner, *Gary Paulsen*

Name: _____

Date: _____

# Handout 31A: Opinion Writing Checklist

**Directions:** Use this checklist to revise your writing. Mark + for "yes" and Δ for "not yet." Ask someone (adult or peer) to evaluate your writing as well.

| Reading Comprehension | Self +/Δ | Peer +/Δ | Teacher +/Δ |
|---|---|---|---|
| Refer to details and examples from both literary and informational texts when explaining key points about the American Revolution | | | |
| Explain historical events related to the American Revolution including what happened and why, based on specific information in a text | | | |
| **Structure** | | | |
| I respond to all parts of the prompt | | | |
| I focus on my opinion throughout | | | |
| I introduce the topic or text clearly in my introduction paragraph | | | |
| I state a clear opinion in my introduction paragraph | | | |
| I organize my ideas into body paragraphs | | | |
| My conclusion paragraph relates to my opinion | | | |
| I use transitions to link paragraphs as well as to link opinions to reasons | | | |
| **Development** | | | |
| I support my opinion with reasons | | | |
| I support my reasons with evidence from text(s) | | | |
| I elaborate upon evidence | | | |
| **Style** | | | |
| I use a variety of sentence patterns (simple, compound, complex) | | | |
| I use vocabulary words that are specific and appropriate to the content | | | |

Name:

Date:

| | | | |
|---|---|---|---|
| My writing style is formal | | | |
| **Conventions** | | | |
| I use progressive verb tenses to make my writing more specific (*he was walking; he is walking; he will be walking*). Underline the words | | | |
| I use one relative adverb to be more specific when describing when, where, or why something happens (underline the clause) | | | |
| I use complete sentences by correcting fragments and run-ons | | | |
| I use correct spelling, capitalization, and punctuation | | | |
| **Writing Process** | | | |
| I revise and edit my writing using the checklist to make it the best it can be | | | |
| **Total # of +'s** | | | |

Name: _____

Date: _____

# Handout 33A: End-of-Module Task Evidence Organizer

**Directions:** Search through the module texts to find evidence for actions the British took against the colonists. Explain the colonists' reactions. Then, record the viewpoints of both the Patriots and the colonists. Be sure to record the text you used in your evidence organizer.

| Question/Purpose: In your opinion, were the American patriots right to fight for their independence from Britain? | | | | |
|---|---|---|---|---|
| Context<br><br>British action | Evidence/Paraphrasing<br><br>How the American Patriots responded | Elaboration/Explanation<br><br>Viewpoint of the Patriots | Elaboration/Explanation<br><br>Viewpoint of the Loyalists | Source<br><br>Where did this information come from? |
| | | | | |
| | | | | |

Name: _____

Date: _____

| | | | | |
|---|---|---|---|---|
| | | | | |
| | | | | |

Name: _____

Date: _____

# Handout 33B: Opinion Writing Checklist

**Directions:** Use this checklist to revise your writing. Mark + for "yes" and Δ for "not yet." Ask someone (adult or peer) to evaluate your writing as well.

| Reading Comprehension | Self +/Δ | Peer +/Δ | Teacher +/Δ |
|---|---|---|---|
| Refer to details and examples from both literary and informational texts when explaining key points about the American Revolution | | | |
| Explain historical events related to the American Revolution including what happened and why, based on specific information in a text | | | |
| **Structure** | | | |
| I respond to all parts of the prompt | | | |
| I focus on my opinion throughout the essay | | | |
| I introduce the topic or text clearly in my introduction paragraph | | | |
| I state a clear opinion in my introduction paragraph | | | |
| I organize my ideas into body paragraphs | | | |
| My conclusion paragraph relates to my opinion | | | |
| I use transitions to link paragraphs as well as to link opinions to reasons | | | |
| **Development** | | | |
| I support my opinion with reasons | | | |
| I support my reasons with evidence from text(s) | | | |
| I elaborate upon evidence | | | |
| **Style** | | | |
| I use a variety of sentence patterns (simple, compound, complex) | | | |
| I use vocabulary words that are specific and appropriate to the content | | | |

Name: _____

Date: _____

| | | | |
|---|---|---|---|
| My writing style is formal | | | |
| **Conventions** | | | |
| I use one relative adverb to be more specific when describing when, where, or why something happens (underline the clause) | | | |
| I use one compound sentence and punctuate it correctly. Circle the conjunction in the compound sentence | | | |
| I use complete sentences by correcting fragments and run-ons | | | |
| I use correct spelling, capitalization, and punctuation | | | |
| **Writing Process** | | | |
| I revise and edit my writing using the checklist to make it the best it can be | | | |
| **Total # of +s** | | | |

Name: _____

Date: _____

# Volume of Reading Reflection Questions

*The Redcoats Are Coming!* Grade 4, Module 3

Student Name: _____

Text: _____

Author: _____

Topic: _____

_____

Genre/type of book: _____

**Directions:** Share what you have learned through reading this text about the American Revolution.

**Informational Text:**

1. Wonder: What might this text teach you about the American Revolution? Provide three details that support your response.

2. Organize: What are the main events or main ideas in this text? Describe the connection between two different ideas or events in the text.

3. Reveal: How does the text rely on illustrations to teach about the American Revolution and to make the information more interesting? Describe at least two things you learned from one powerful illustration the author uses.

Name: _____

Date: _____

4. Distill: Based on the information presented in the book, what is one of the author's main points about the American Revolution? How does he or she support the points?

5. Know: How did this text build your knowledge? Explain how the information you learned in this text built on your knowledge from other texts. Connect the information between the two texts with specific examples.

6. Vocabulary: Write three important vocabulary words and definitions that you learned in this text. What makes them important words to know?

**Literary Text**

1. Wonder: What about the front and/or back covers drew you to this story?

2. Organize: Write a short summary of the story including the major character(s), setting, problem, and resolution.

3. Reveal: Is this story told in first person or third person? What other literary work have you read in this module that is told from this point of view?

4. Distill: What is a theme of this story? Provide evidence from the text to support your response.

5. Know: How does the information about the American Revolution in this story build on what you have already learned in this study in class?

6. Vocabulary: Write three important vocabulary words and definitions that you learned in this text. What makes them important words to know?

# *WIT & WISDOM* Parent Tip Sheet

## WHAT IS MY GRADE 4 STUDENT LEARNING IN MODULE 3?

*Wit & Wisdom* is our English curriculum. It builds knowledge of key topics in history, science, and literature through the study of excellent texts. By reading and responding to stories and nonfiction texts, we will build knowledge of the following topics:

Module 1: A Great Heart

Module 2: Extreme Settings

**Module 3: The Redcoats Are Coming!**

Module 4: Myth Making

In the third module, The Redcoats Are Coming!, we will use a critical eye to see how the American Revolution was a foundation for American history. With a focus on identifying and understanding perspective and its impact on our understanding of events and decisions people make, students will gain greater skill in the area of critical thinking as both readers and writers. We will ask the question: why is it important to understand all sides of a story?

## OUR CLASS WILL READ THESE BOOKS:

### Novel (Literary)

- *Woods Runner*, Gary Paulsen

### Picture Book (Literary)

- *The Scarlet Stockings Spy*, Trina Hakes Noble

### Historical Account (Informational)

- *George vs. George: The American Revolution as Seen from Both Sides*, Rosalyn Schanzer

### Poetry

- *Colonial Voices: Hear Them Speak*, Kay Winters

## OUR CLASS WILL EXAMINE THIS PAINTING:

- *Washington Crossing the Delaware*, Emanuel Leutze

## OUR CLASS WILL EXAMINE THIS ENGRAVING:

- *The Boston Massacre*, Paul Revere

## OUR CLASS WILL READ THESE ARTICLES:

- "Massacre in King Street," Mark Clemens
- "Detested Tea," Andrew Matthews

## OUR CLASS WILL WATCH THESE VIDEOS:

- "Paul Revere-Mini Biography"
- "Fred Woods Trail—Driftwood, Pennsylvania"
- "The Culper Spy Ring: Path through History"
- "REBUILD—From The Ashes, The World Trade Center Rises Again"

## OUR CLASS WILL VIEW THIS PHOTOGRAPH:

- *Raising the Flag at Ground Zero*, Thomas E. Franklin

## OUR CLASS WILL VISIT THESE WEBSITES:

- EDSITEment: Emanuel Leutze's Symbolic Scene of *Washington Crossing the Delaware* (**http://witeng.link/0158**)
- The Gilder Lehrman Institute of American History (**http://witeng.link/0209**)

## OUR CLASS WILL ASK THESE QUESTIONS:

1. What were the perspectives of the two main sides of the American Revolution?
2. How did different people's experiences affect their perspectives about the American Revolution?
3. How did different people's perspectives affect their actions during the American Revolution?
4. What drove the Patriots to fight for their independence from Britain?

## QUESTIONS TO ASK AT HOME:

As your Grade 4 student reads, ask:

- What is happening in the story?
- What is the essential meaning, or most important message, in this book?
- How does this story build your knowledge about the American Revolution?

# BOOKS TO READ AT HOME:

- *Can't You Make Them Behave, King George?*, Jean Fritz
- *For Liberty: The Story of the Boston Massacre*, Timothy Decker
- *Chains*, Laurie Halse Anderson
- *Forge*, Laurie Halse Anderson
- *Johnny Tremain*, Esther Hoskins Forbes
- *My Brother Sam is Dead*, James Lincoln Collier
- *George Washington, Spymaster*, Thomas B. Allen
- *Sophia's War: A Tale of the Revolution*, Avi
- *Sam the Minuteman*, Nathaniel Benchley
- *If You Lived in the Times of the American Revolution*, Kay Moore
- *Did it All Start with a Snowball Fight?*, Mary Kay Carson
- *Sybil Ludington's Midnight Ride*, Marsha Amstel
- *Samuel's Choice*, Richard Berleth

# IDEAS FOR TALKING ABOUT THE AMERICAN REVOLUTION:

Ask your Grade 4 student to explain the perspectives of the two main sides in the American Revolution.

Explain the perspective of each group of colonists about the tax on tea (Patriots, Loyalists, In-Betweens).

Summarize what was happening in the books read in class.

Create a comic strip story map to record in pictures what is happening in each story that is read in class. Discuss with your child each night.

Practice telling a story about the American Revolution in first-person (I, me, we) and third-person (he, she, they).

Practice reading aloud a monologue assigned for homework. Ask your Grade 4 student how the colonists feel about the tea tax and why.

Discuss the American Spirit that kept Patriots fighting in the war despite terrible conditions and odds of winning.

Discuss the characters in *The Scarlet Stockings Spy* and *Woods Runner*. Who are they? Why are they important to the stories?

Discuss whether or not the Patriots were justified in fighting for their independence from Britain. What was the cost of the war for each side in the conflict?

## CREDITS

Great Minds® has made every effort to obtain permission for the reprinting of all copyrighted material. If any owner of copyrighted material is not acknowledged herein, please contact Great Minds® for proper acknowledgment in all future editions and reprints of this module.

- All images are used under license from Shutterstock.com unless otherwise noted.

- All material from the *Common Core State Standards for English Language Arts & Literacy in History/Social Studies, Science, and Technical Subjects* © Copyright 2010 National Governors Association Center for Best Practices and Council of Chief State School Officers. All rights reserved.

- The Painted Essay® is used by permission of Diana Leddy.

- Handout 4A: "Massacre in King Street" by Mark Clemens from *Road to Revolution*, Cobblestone September 2014. Text copyright © 2014 by Carus Publishing Company. Reprinted by permission of Cricket Media. All Cricket Media material is copyrighted by Carus Publishing d/b/a Cricket Media, and/or various authors and illustrators. Any commercial use or distribution of material without permission is strictly prohibited. Please visit http://www.cricketmedia.com/info/licensing2 for licensing and http://www.cricketmedia.com for subscriptions.

- Handout 13A: "Detested Tea" by Andrew Matthews from *Road to Revolution*, Cobblestone September 2014. Text copyright © 2014 by Carus Publishing Company. Reprinted by permission of Cricket Media. All Cricket Media material is copyrighted by Carus Publishing d/b/a Cricket Media, and/or various authors and illustrators. Any commercial use or distribution of material without permission is strictly prohibited. Please visit http://www.cricketmedia.com/info/licensing2 for licensing and http://www.cricketmedia.com for subscriptions.

- For updated credit information, please visit http://witeng.link/credits.

## ACKNOWLEDGMENTS

### Great Minds® Staff

*The following writers, editors, reviewers, and support staff contributed to the development of this curriculum.*

Ann Brigham, Lauren Chapalee, Sara Clarke, Emily Climer, Lorraine Griffith, Emily Gula, Sarah Henchey, Trish Huerster, Stephanie Kane-Mainier, Lior Klirs, Liz Manolis, Andrea Minich, Lynne Munson, Marya Myers, Rachel Rooney, Aaron Schifrin, Danielle Shylit, Rachel Stack, Sarah Turnage, Michelle Warner, Amy Wierzbicki, Margaret Wilson, and Sarah Woodard.

### Colleagues and Contributors

*We are grateful for the many educators, writers, and subject-matter experts who made this program possible.*

David Abel, Robin Agurkis, Elizabeth Bailey, Julianne Barto, Amy Benjamin, Andrew Biemiller, Charlotte Boucher, Sheila Byrd-Carmichael, Eric Carey, Jessica Carloni, Janine Cody, Rebecca Cohen, Elaine Collins, Tequila Cornelious, Beverly Davis, Matt Davis, Thomas Easterling, Jeanette Edelstein, Kristy Ellis, Moira Clarkin Evans, Charles Fischer, Marty Gephart, Kath Gibbs, Natalie Goldstein, Christina Gonzalez, Mamie Goodson, Nora Graham, Lindsay Griffith, Brenna Haffner, Joanna Hawkins, Elizabeth Haydel, Steve Hettleman, Cara Hoppe, Ashley Hymel, Carol Jago, Jennifer Johnson, Mason Judy, Gail Kearns, Shelly Knupp, Sarah Kushner, Shannon Last, Suzanne Lauchaire, Diana Leddy, David Liben, Farren Liben, Jennifer Marin, Susannah Maynard, Cathy McGath, Emily McKean, Jane Miller, Rebecca Moore, Cathy Newton, Turi Nilsson, Julie Norris, Galemarie Ola, Michelle Palmieri, Meredith Phillips, Shilpa Raman, Tonya Romayne, Emmet Rosenfeld, Jennifer Ruppel, Mike Russoniello, Deborah Samley, Casey Schultz, Renee Simpson, Rebecca Sklepovich, Amelia Swabb, Kim Taylor, Vicki Taylor, Melissa Thomson, Lindsay Tomlinson, Melissa Vail, Keenan Walsh, Julia Wasson, Lynn Welch, Yvonne Guerrero Welch, Emily Whyte, Lynn Woods, and Rachel Zindler.

### Early Adopters

*The following early adopters provided invaluable insight and guidance for* Wit & Wisdom:

- Bourbonnais School District 53 • Bourbonnais, IL
- Coney Island Prep Middle School • Brooklyn, NY
- Gate City Charter School for the Arts • Merrimack, NH
- Hebrew Academy for Special Children • Brooklyn, NY
- Paris Independent Schools • Paris, KY
- Saydel Community School District • Saydel, IA
- Strive Collegiate Academy • Nashville, TN
- Valiente College Preparatory Charter School • South Gate, CA
- Voyageur Academy • Detroit, MI

Design Direction provided by Alton Creative, Inc.

Project management support, production design, and copyediting services provided by ScribeConcepts.com

Copyediting services provided by Fine Lines Editing

Product management support provided by Sandhill Consulting